Dash Diet Co

Easy Recipes to Save Money and
Time.
Lose Weight, Cut Cholesterol and
Prevent Hypertension with
Mediterranean and Dash Solution.
Lower your Blood Pressure with Quick
and Easy Recipes.

America Daily Cooking

Additionally, the information in the following pages is intended only for informational purposes and should thus be thought of as universal. As befitting its nature, it is presented without assurance regarding its prolonged validity or interim quality. Trademarks that are mentioned are done without written consent and can in no way be considered an endorsement from the trademark holder.

Table of Contents

Introduction

The DASH diet leans heavily on vegetables, fruits, and whole grains. Fish and lean poultry are served moderately. Whole wheat flour is used instead of white flour. DASH as a diet plan promotes the consumption of low-fat dairy, lean meat, fruits, and vegetables. It is literally a mix of old world and new world eating plans. It has been designed to follow old world diet principles to help eliminate new world health problems.

The carbohydrates are mainly made of plant fiber which the body does not easily digest and therefore cannot turn into stored fat. The plan is rich in good fats that make food taste good and help us feel fuller for a longer period of time. Proteins are not forbidden but are geared more toward plant-based protein and not so much meat consumption.

When filling the plate for a meal, it is important that the food be attractive as well as tasty and nutritious. A wide variety of foods will make this plan much more interesting. Try to make choices that will offer a range of colors and textures. And remember that dessert is not off limits but should be based around healthy choices that include fresh fruit.

The DASH eating plans emphasis on vegetables, fruits, whole grains, and low-fat dairy products makes it an ideal plan for anyone looking to gain health through lowered blood pressure and a healthier heart. It is a heart healthy way of eating. The DASH plan has no specialized recipes or food plans. Daily caloric intake depends on a person's activity level and age. People who need to lose weight would naturally eat fewer calories.

The DASH diet's major focus is on grains, vegetables, and fruits because these foods are higher fiber foods and will make you feel full longer. Whole grains should be consumed six to eight times daily, vegetables four to six servings daily, and fruit four to five servings daily. Low-fat dairy is an important part of the diet and should be eaten two to three times daily. And there should be six or fewer servings daily of fish, poultry, and lean meat.

The DASH diet focuses on long-term healthy eating habits. The diet doesn't force you to starve or battle constant cravings. Instead, it focuses on understanding food groups, controlling portion sizes, and making sure you get the optimal levels of potassium, calcium, magnesium, fiber, and protein. The diet focuses certain food groups for specific reasons: Fruits and vegetables give you the magnesium and potassium your body needs, and low-fat dairy products provide calcium. Every food you eat should have a purpose, and that's the most important principle of the DASH diet: eat well so you feel well. Here are some additional points to remember when you're following the DASH principles:

Reduce your sodium intake. The diet recommends less than 2,300 mg of sodium per day. The National Heart, Lung and Blood Institute recommends lowering the sodium intake even further—to 1,500 mg—for people with high blood pressure, people with diabetes or chronic kidney disease, African Americans, and people aged 51 and over.

Eat fruits, vegetables, and low-fat dairy products

Focus on high-fiber foods

Eat more healthy fats, which are good for your heart, instead of saturated fats

Achieve and maintain a healthy body weight

Eat a lot of potassium and magnesium

Stay hydrated by drinking plenty of plain water

Avoid smoking

The DASH diet is more than just a diet—it's a lifestyle.

Sides

Flavored Turnips Mix

Preparation time: 10 minutes

Cooking time: 15 minutes

Servings: 4

Ingredients:

- 1 tablespoon lemon juice
- Zest of 2 oranges, grated
- 16 ounces turnips, sliced
- 3 tablespoons olive oil
- 1 tablespoon rosemary, chopped
- Black pepper to the taste

Directions:

1. Heat up a pan with the oil over medium-high heat, add turnips, stir and cook for 5 minutes.

2. Add lemon juice, black pepper, orange zest and rosemary, stir, cook for 10 minutes

more, divide between plates and serve as a side dish.

3. Enjoy!

Nutrition: calories 130, fat 1, fiber 2, carbs 8, protein 4

Lemony Fennel Mix

Preparation time: 10 minutes

Cooking time: 0 minutes

Servings: 4

Ingredients:

- 3 tablespoons lemon juice
- 1 pound fennel, chopped
- 2 tablespoons olive oil
- A pinch of black pepper

Directions:

1. In a salad bowl, mix fennel with and black pepper, oil and lemon juice, toss well, divide between plates and serve as a side dish.

2. Enjoy!

Nutrition: calories 130, fat 1, fiber 1, carbs 7, protein 7

Simple Cauliflower Mix

Preparation time: 10 minutes

Cooking time: 35 minutes

Servings: 4

Ingredients:

- 6 cups cauliflower florets
- 2 teaspoons sweet paprika
- 2 cups chicken stock
- ¼ cup avocado oil
- Black pepper to the taste

Directions:

1. In a baking dish, combine the cauliflower with stock, oil, black pepper and paprika, toss, introduce in the oven and bake at 375 degrees F for 35 minutes.

2. Divide between plates and serve as a side dish.

3. Enjoy!

Nutrition: calories 180, fat 3, fiber 2, carbs 46, protein 6

Broccoli Mix

Preparation time: 10 minutes

Cooking time: 3 hours

Servings: 10

Ingredients:

- 6 cups broccoli florets
- 10 ounces tomato sauce, sodium-free
- 1 and ½ cups low-fat cheddar cheese, shredded
- ½ teaspoon cider vinegar
- ¼ cup yellow onion, chopped
- A pinch of black pepper
- 2 tablespoons olive oil

Directions:

1. Grease your slow cooker with the oil, add broccoli, tomato sauce, cider vinegar, onion and black pepper, cover and cook on High for 2 hours and 30 minutes.

2. Sprinkle the cheese all over, cover, cook on High for 30 minutes more, divide between plates and serve as a side dish.

3. Enjoy!

Nutrition: calories 160, fat 6, fiber 4, carbs 11, protein 6

Tasty Bean Side Dish

Preparation time: 10 minutes

Cooking time: 5 hours

Servings: 10

Ingredients:

- 1 and ½ cups tomato sauce, salt-free

- 1 yellow onion, chopped
- 2 celery ribs, chopped
- 1 sweet red pepper, chopped
- 1 green bell pepper, chopped
- ½ cup water
- 2 bay leaves
- 1 teaspoon ground mustard
- 1 tablespoon cider vinegar
- 16 ounces canned kidney beans, no-salt-added, drained and rinsed
- 16 ounces canned black-eyed peas, no-salt-added, drained and rinsed
- 15 ounces corn
- 15 ounces canned lima beans, no-salt-added, drained and rinsed
- 15 ounces canned black beans, no-salt-added, drained and rinsed

Directions:

1.   In your slow cooker, mix the tomato sauce with the onion, celery, red pepper, green bell pepper, water, bay leaves, mustard, vinegar, kidney beans, black-eyed peas, corn, lima beans and black beans, cover and cook on Low for 5 hours.

2. Discard bay leaves, divide the whole mix between plates and serve.

3. Enjoy!

Nutrition: calories 211, fat 4, fiber 8, carbs 20, protein 7

Easy Green Beans

Preparation time: 10 minutes

Cooking time: 2 hours

Servings: 12

Ingredients:

- 16 ounces green beans
- 3 tablespoons olive oil
- ½ cup coconut sugar
- 1 teaspoon low-sodium soy sauce
- ½ teaspoon garlic powder

Directions:

1. In your slow cooker, mix the green beans with the oil, sugar, soy sauce and garlic powder, cover and cook on Low for 2 hours.

2. Toss the beans, divide them between plates and serve as a side dish.

3. Enjoy!

Nutrition: calories 142, fat 7, fiber 4, carbs 15, protein 3

Creamy Corn

Preparation time: 10 minutes

Cooking time: 4 hours

Servings: 12

Ingredients:

- 10 cups corn
- 20 ounces fat-free cream cheese
- ½ cup fat-free milk
- ½ cup low-fat butter
- A pinch of black pepper
- 2 tablespoons green onions, chopped

Directions:

1. In your slow cooker, mix the corn with cream cheese, milk, butter, black pepper and onions, toss, cover and cook on Low for 4 hours.

2. Toss one more time, divide between plates and serve as a side dish.

3. Enjoy!

Nutrition: calories 256, fat 11, fiber 2, carbs 17, protein 5

Classic Peas and Carrots

Preparation time: 10 minutes

Cooking time: 5 hours

Servings: 12

Ingredients:

- 1 pound carrots, sliced
- ¼ cup water
- 1 yellow onion, chopped
- 2 tablespoons olive oil
- 2 tablespoons stevia
- 4 garlic cloves, minced
- 1 teaspoon marjoram, dried
- A pinch of white pepper
- 16 ounces peas

Directions:

1. In your slow cooker, mix the carrots with water, onion, oil, stevia, garlic, marjoram, white pepper and peas, toss, cover and cook on High for 5 hours.

2. Divide between plates and serve as a side dish.

3. Enjoy!

Nutrition: calories 107, fat 3, fiber 3, carbs 14, protein 4

Mushroom Pilaf

Preparation time: 10 minutes

Cooking time: 3 hours

Servings: 6

Ingredients:

- 1 cup wild rice
- 2 garlic cloves, minced
- 6 green onions, chopped
- 2 tablespoons olive oil
- ½ pound baby Bella mushrooms
- 2 cups water

Directions:

1. In your slow cooker, mix the rice with garlic, onions, oil, mushrooms and water, toss, cover and cook on Low for 3 hours.

2. Stir the pilaf one more time, divide between plates and serve.

3. Enjoy!

Nutrition: calories 210, fat 7, fiber 1, carbs 16, protein 4

Butternut Mix

Preparation time: 10 minutes

Cooking time: 4 hours

Servings: 8

Ingredients:

- 1 cup carrots, chopped
- 1 tablespoon olive oil
- 1 yellow onion, chopped
- ½ teaspoon stevia
- 1 garlic clove, minced
- ½ teaspoon curry powder
- ½ teaspoon cinnamon powder
- ¼ teaspoon ginger, grated
- 1 butternut squash, cubed
- 2 and ½ cups low-sodium veggie stock
- ½ cup basmati rice
- ¾ cup coconut milk

Directions:

1.	Heat up a pan with the oil over medium- high heat, add the oil, onion, garlic, stevia, carrots, curry powder, cinnamon and ginger, stir, cook for 5 minutes and transfer to your slow cooker.

2. Add squash, stock and coconut milk, stir, cover and cook on Low for 4 hours.

3. Divide the butternut mix between plates and serve as a side dish.

4. Enjoy!

Nutrition: calories 200, fat 4, fiber 4, carbs 17, protein 3

Sausage Side Dish

Preparation time: 10 minutes

Cooking time: 2 hours

Servings: 12

Ingredients:

- 1 pound no-sugar, beef sausage, chopped
- 2 tablespoons olive oil
- ½ pound mushrooms, chopped
- 6 celery ribs, chopped
- 2 yellow onions, chopped
- 2 garlic cloves, minced
- 1 tablespoon sage, dried
- 1 cup low-sodium veggie stock
- 1 cup cranberries, dried
- ½ cup sunflower seeds, peeled
- 1 whole wheat bread loaf, cubed

Directions:

1. Heat up a pan with the oil over medium- high heat, add beef, stir and brown for a few minutes.

2. Add mushrooms, onion, celery, garlic and sage, stir, cook for a few more minutes and transfer to your slow cooker.

3. Add stock, cranberries, sunflower seeds and the bread cubes, cover and cook on High for 2 hours.

4. Stir the whole mix, divide between plates and serve as a side dish.

5. Enjoy!

Nutrition: calories 200, fat 3, fiber 6, carbs 13, protein 4

Easy Potatoes Mix

Preparation time: 10 minutes

Cooking time: 6 hours

Servings: 8

Ingredients:

- 16 baby red potatoes, halved

- 1 carrot, sliced
- 1 celery rib, chopped
- ¼ cup yellow onion, chopped
- 2 cups low-sodium chicken stock
- 1 tablespoon parsley, chopped
- A pinch of black pepper
- 1 garlic clove minced
- 2 tablespoons olive oil

Directions:

1.   In your slow cooker, mix the potatoes with the carrot, celery, onion, stock, parsley, garlic, oil and black pepper, toss, cover and cook on Low for 6 hours.

2. Divide between plates and serve as a side dish.

3. Enjoy!

Nutrition: calories 114, fat 3, fiber 3, carbs 18, protein 4

Black-Eyed Peas Mix

Preparation time: 10 minutes

Cooking time: 5 hours

Servings: 12

Ingredients:

- 17 ounces black-eyed peas
- ½ cup sausage, chopped
- 1 yellow onion, chopped
- 1 sweet red pepper, chopped
- 1 jalapeno, chopped
- 2 garlic cloves minced
- ½ teaspoon cumin, ground
- A pinch of black pepper
- 6 cups water
- 2 tablespoons cilantro, chopped

Directions:

1.   In your slow cooker, mix the peas with the sausage, onion, red pepper, jalapeno, garlic, cumin, black pepper, water and cilantro, cover and cook on Low for 5 hours.

2. Divide between plates and serve as a side dish.

3. Enjoy!

Nutrition: calories 170, fat 3, fiber 7, carbs 20, protein 13

Green Beans and Corn Mix

Preparation time: 10 minutes

Cooking time: 4 hours

Servings: 8

Ingredients:

- 15 ounces green beans
- 14 ounces corn

- 11 ounces cream of mushroom soup, low-fat and sodium-free
- 4 ounces mushrooms, sliced
- ½ cup almonds, chopped
- ½ cup low-fat cheddar cheese, shredded
- ½ cup low-fat sour cream

Directions:

1.   In your slow cooker, mix the green beans with the corn, mushrooms soup, mushrooms, almonds, cheese and sour cream, toss, cover and cook on Low for 4 hours.

2. Stir one more time, divide between plates and serve as a side dish.

3. Enjoy!

Nutrition: calories 211, fat 8, fiber 3, carbs 16, protein 4

Spiced Carrots

Preparation time: 10 minutes

Cooking time: 6 hours

Servings: 6

Ingredients:

- 2 pounds small carrots, peeled
- ½ cup low-fat butter, melted
- ½ cup canned peach, unsweetened
- 3 tablespoons stevia
- ½ teaspoon cinnamon powder
- 1 teaspoon vanilla extract
- A pinch of nutmeg, ground
- 2 tablespoons water
- 2 tablespoons cornstarch

Directions:

1. In your slow cooker, mix the carrots with the butter, peach, stevia, cinnamon, vanilla, nutmeg and cornstarch mixed with water, toss, cover and cook on Low for 6 hours.

2. Toss the carrots one more time, divide between plates and serve as a side dish.

3. Enjoy!

Nutrition: calories 200, fat 12, fiber 4, carbs 20, protein 3

Squash and Grains Mix

Preparation time: 10 minutes

Cooking time: 4 hours

Servings: 12

Ingredients:

- 1 butternut squash, peeled and cubed
- 1 cup whole grain blend, uncooked
- 1 yellow onion, chopped
- 3 garlic cloves, minced
- ½ cup water
- 2 teaspoons thyme, chopped
- A pinch of black pepper
- 12 ounces low-sodium veggie stock
- 6 ounces baby spinach

Directions:

1. In your slow cooker, mix the squash with whole grain, onion, garlic, water, thyme, black pepper, stock and spinach, cover and cook on Low for 4 hours.

2. Divide between plates and serve as a side dish.

3. Enjoy!

Nutrition: calories 100, fat 1, fiber 4, carbs 22, protein 3

Mushroom Mix

Preparation time: 10 minutes

Cooking time: 4 hours

Servings: 6

Ingredients:

- 1 pound mushrooms, halved
- 3 tablespoons olive oil
- 1 yellow onion, chopped
- 1 teaspoon Italian seasoning
- 1 cup tomato sauce, no-salt-added

Directions:

1. In your slow cooker, mix the mushrooms with the oil, onion, Italian seasoning and tomato sauce, toss, cover and cook on Low for 4 hours.

2. Divide between plates and serve as a side dish.

3. Enjoy!

Nutrition: calories 100, fat 5, fiber 2, carbs 9, protein 4

Spinach and Rice

Preparation time: 10 minutes

Cooking time: 4 hours

Servings: 8

Ingredients:

- 2 tablespoons olive oil
- 1 yellow onion, chopped
- ¼ teaspoon thyme, dried
- 2 garlic cloves, minced
- 4 cups low-sodium chicken stock
- 20 ounces spinach, chopped
- 8 ounces fat-free cream cheese
- 2 cups wild rice
- 2 cups low-fat cheddar cheese, shredded
- ½ cup whole wheat bread, crumbled

Directions:

1. In your slow cooker, mix the oil with the onion, thyme, garlic, stock, spinach, cream cheese and rice, toss, cover and cook on Low for 4 hours.

2. Add the cheese and the breadcrumbs, cover the pot, leave it aside for a few minutes, divide between plates and serve as a side dish.

3. Enjoy!

Nutrition: calories 199, fat 2, fiber 6, carbs 9, protein 6

Creamy Mushrooms Mix

Preparation time: 10 minutes

Cooking time: 8 hours

Servings: 8

Ingredients:

- 1 and ½ pounds cremini mushrooms, halved
- 2 garlic cloves, minced
- 1 shallot, chopped
- ¼ cup low sodium chicken stock
- 2 tablespoons parsley, chopped
- ½ cup coconut cream
- 1 teaspoon cornstarch

Directions:

1.   In your slow cooker, mix the mushrooms with garlic, shallot, stock and parsley, cover and cook on Low for 7 hours.

2. Add coconut cream mixed with the cornstarch, cover, cook on Low for 1 more hour, divide between plates and serve as a side dish.

3. Enjoy!

Nutrition: calories 188, fat 3, fiber 8, carbs 17, protein 4

Ginger Beets

Preparation time: 10 minutes

Cooking time: 6 hours

Servings: 8

Ingredients:

- 6 beets, peeled and sliced
- 1 teaspoon orange peel, grated
- 2 tablespoons stevia
- 1/3 cup orange juice
- 2 tablespoons white vinegar
- 2 tablespoons olive oil
- 1 tablespoon ginger, grated
- A pinch of black pepper

Directions:

1.   In your slow cooker, mix the beets with the orange peel, orange juice, stevia, vinegar, oil, ginger and black pepper, toss, cover and cook on Low for 6 hours.

2. Divide between plates and serve as a side dish.

3. Enjoy!

Nutrition: calories 177, fat 2, fiber 7, carbs 11, protein 3

Artichokes Mix

Preparation time: 10 minutes

Cooking time: 5 hours

Servings: 8

Ingredients:

- 4 artichokes, trimmed and halved
- 2 cups whole wheat breadcrumbs
- 1 tablespoon olive oil
- Juice of 1 lemon
- 3 garlic cloves, minced
- 1/3 cup low-fat parmesan, grated
- 1 tablespoon lemon zest, grated
- 2 tablespoons parsley, chopped
- Black pepper to the taste
- 1 cup low-sodium vegetable stock
- 1 tablespoon shallot, minced
- 1 teaspoon oregano, chopped

Directions:

1. Rub artichokes with the lemon juice and the oil and put them in your slow cooker.

2. Add breadcrumbs, garlic, parsley, parmesan, lemon zest, black pepper, shallot, oregano and stock, cover and cook on Low for 5 hours.

3. Divide the whole mix between plates, sprinkle parsley on top and serve as a side dish.

4. Enjoy!

Nutrition: calories 200, fat 4, fiber 4, carbs 10, protein 6

Asparagus Mix

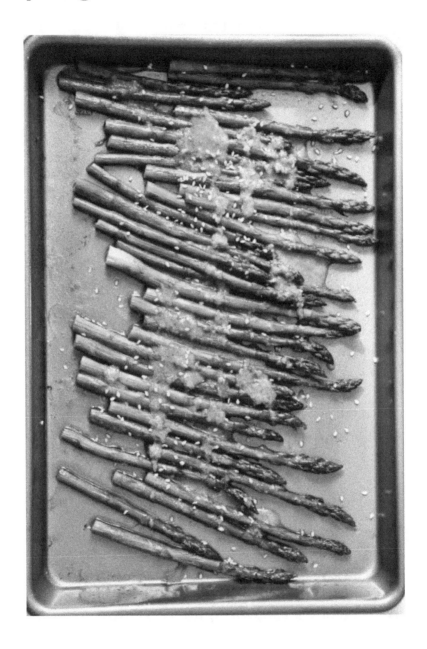

Preparation time: 10 minutes

Cooking time: 2 hours

Servings: 4

Ingredients:

- 1 pound asparagus, trimmed and halved
- 1 tablespoon parsley, chopped
- ½ cup low-sodium veggie stock
- 1 garlic clove, minced
- ¼ teaspoon lemon zest, grated
- 2 teaspoons lemon juice

Directions:

1.   In your slow cooker, mix the asparagus with the parsley, stock, garlic, lemon zest and lemon juice, toss a bit, cover and cook on High for 2 hours.

2. Divide the asparagus between plates and serve as a side dish.

3. Enjoy!

Nutrition: calories 130, fat 3, fiber 2, carbs 10, protein 4

Black Bean and Corn Mix

Preparation time: 10 minutes

Cooking time: 6 hours

Servings: 6

Ingredients:

- 4 tomatoes, chopped
- 1 cup corn kernels
- 16 ounces canned black beans, drained
- 2 garlic cloves, minced
- ½ cup parsley, chopped
- 1 small red onion, chopped
- 1 red bell pepper, chopped
- Juice of 1 lemon
- 2 tablespoons stevia

Directions:

1.   In your slow cooker, mix the tomatoes with corn, black beans, garlic, parsley, lemon juice, bell pepper, onion and stevia, toss, cook on Low for 6 hours, divide between plates and serve as a side dish.

2. Enjoy!

Nutrition: calories 210, fat 1, fiber 5, carbs 15, protein 7

Celery Mix

Preparation time: 10 minutes

Cooking time: 3 hours

Servings: 3

Ingredients:

- 2 celery roots, cut into medium wedges
- 1 cup low-sodium veggie stock
- 1 teaspoon mustard
- ¼ cup low-fat sour cream
- Black pepper to the taste
- 2 teaspoons thyme, chopped

Directions:

1. In your slow cooker, mix the celery with the stock, mustard, cream, black pepper and thyme, cover and cook on High for 3 hours.

2. Divide the celery between plates, drizzle some of the cooking juices on top and serve as a side dish.

3. Enjoy!

Nutrition: calories 160, fat 2, fiber 1, carbs 7, protein 4

Kale Side Dish

Preparation time: 10 minutes

Cooking time: 2 hours

Servings: 6

Ingredients:

- 1 pound kale, chopped
- 2 teaspoons olive oil
- 4 garlic cloves, minced
- ½ cup low-sodium veggie stock
- 1 tablespoons lemon juice
- 1 cup cherry tomatoes, halved
- Black pepper to the taste

Directions:

1. Heat up a pan with the oil over medium heat, add garlic, stir, cook for 2 minutes and transfer to your slow cooker.

2. Add kale, stock, tomatoes, black pepper and lemon juice, cover, cook on High for 2 hours.

3. Divide the whole mix between plates and serve as a side dish.

4. Enjoy!

Nutrition: calories 160, fat 2, fiber 3, carbs 8, protein 4

Spicy Eggplant

Preparation time: 10 minutes

Cooking time: 3 hours

Servings: 4

Ingredients:

- 1 eggplant, sliced
- ½ teaspoon cumin, ground
- 1 teaspoon mustard seed
- ½ teaspoon coriander, ground
- ½ teaspoon curry powder
- A pinch of nutmeg, ground
- 2 cups cherry tomatoes, halved
- ½ yellow onion, chopped
- 1 tablespoon olive oil
- 1 garlic clove, minced
- 1 teaspoon red wine vinegar
- Black pepper to the taste
- 1 tablespoon cilantro, chopped

Directions:

1. Grease the slow cooker with the oil and add eggplant slices inside.

2. Add cumin, mustard seeds, coriander, curry powder, nutmeg, tomatoes, onion, garlic,

vinegar, black pepper and cilantro, cover and cook on High for 3 hours.

3. Divide between plates and serve as a side dish.

4. Enjoy!

Nutrition: calories 180, fat 4, fiber 5, carbs 20, protein 4

Corn Salad

Preparation time: 10 minutes

Cooking time: 2 hours

Servings: 6

Ingredients:

- 2 ounces prosciutto, cut into strips
- 1 teaspoon olive oil
- 2 cups corn
- ½ cup salt-free tomato sauce
- 1 teaspoon garlic, minced
- 1 green bell pepper, chopped

Directions:

1. Grease your slow cooker with the oil, add corn, prosciutto, tomato sauce, garlic and bell pepper, cover and cook on High for 2 hours.

2. Divide between plates and serve as a side dish.

3. Enjoy!

Nutrition: calories 109, fat 2, fiber 2, carbs 10, protein 5

Spiced Cabbage

Preparation time: 10 minutes

Cooking time: 4 hours

Servings: 6

Ingredients:

- 2 yellow onions, chopped
- 10 cups red cabbage, shredded
- 1 cup plums, pitted and chopped
- 1 teaspoon cinnamon powder
- 1 garlic clove, minced
- 1 teaspoon cumin seeds
- ¼ teaspoon cloves, ground
- 2 tablespoons red wine vinegar
- 1 teaspoon coriander seeds
- ½ cup water

Directions:

1. In your slow cooker, mix cabbage with onions, plums, garlic, cinnamon, cumin, cloves, vinegar, coriander and water, stir, cover and cook on Low for 4 hours.

2. Divide between plates and serve as a side dish.

3. Enjoy!

Nutrition: calories 197, fat 1, fiber 5, carbs 14, protein 3

Seafood

Steamed Salmon Teriyaki

Preparation time: 10 minutes

Servings: 4

Cooking time: 15 minutes

Ingredients:

- 3 green onions, minced
- 2 packet Stevia
- 1 tbsp freshly grated ginger
- 1 clove garlic, minced
- 2 tsp. sesame seeds
- 1 tbsp sesame oil
- ¼ cup mirin
- 2 tbsp low sodium soy sauce
- 1/2-lb salmon filet

Directions:

1. Place a large saucepan on medium high fire. Place a trivet inside saucepan and fill pan halfway with water. Cover and bring to a boil.

2. Meanwhile in a heat-proof dish that fits inside saucepan, mix well stevia, ginger, garlic, oil, mirin, and soy sauce. Add salmon and cover well with sauce.

3. Top salmon with sesame seeds and green onions. Cover dish with foil.

4. Place on top of trivet. Cover and steam for 15 minutes.

5. Let it rest for 5 minutes in pan.

6. Serve and enjoy.

Nutrition:

Calories: 242.7; Carbs: 1.2g; Protein: 35.4g; Fats: 10.7g; Saturated Fat: 2.1g; Sodium: 285mg

Easy Steamed Alaskan Cod

Preparation time: 10 minutes

Servings: 3

Cooking time: 15 minutes

Ingredients:

- 2 tbsp butter
- Pepper to taste
- 1 cup cherry tomatoes, halved
- 1 large Wild Alaskan cod filet, cut into 3 smaller pieces

Directions:

1.   Place a large saucepan on medium high fire. Place a trivet inside saucepan and fill pan halfway with water. Cover and bring to a boil.

2. Meanwhile in a heat-proof dish that fits inside saucepan, add all ingredients.

3. Cover dish with a foil. Place on trivet and steam for 15 minutes.

4. Serve and enjoy.

Nutrition:

Calories: 132.9; Carbs: 1.9g; Protein: 12.2g; Fats: 8.5g; Saturated Fat: 4.9g; Sodium: 296mg

Dill and Lemon Cod Packets

Preparation time: 10 minutes

Servings: 2

Cooking time: 10 minutes

Ingredients:

- 2 tsp. olive oil, divided
- 4 slices lemon, divided
- 2 sprigs fresh dill, divide
- ½ tsp. garlic powder, divided
- Pepper to taste
- 1/2-lb cod filets

Directions:

1.   Place a large saucepan on medium high fire. Place a trivet inside saucepan and fill pan halfway with water. Cover and bring to a boil.

2. Cut two pieces of 15-inch lengths foil.

3. In one foil, place one filet in the middle. Season with pepper to taste. Sprinkle ¼ tsp. garlic. Add a tsp. of oil on top of filet. Top with 2 slices of lemon and a sprig of dill. Fold

over the foil and seal the filet inside. Repeat process for remaining fish.

4. Place packet on trivet. Cover and steam for 10 minutes.

5. Serve and enjoy.

Nutrition:

Calories: 164.8; Carbs: 9.4g; Protein: 18.3g; Fats: 6g; Saturated Fat: 1g; Sodium: 347mg

Steamed Fish Mediterranean Style

Preparation time: 10 minutes

Servings: 4

Cooking time: 15 minutes

Ingredients:

- Pepper to taste
- 1 clove garlic, smashed
- 2 tsp. olive oil
- 1 bunch fresh thyme
- 2 tbsp pickled capers
- 1 cup black salt-cured olives

- 1-lb cherry tomatoes, halved
- 1 ½-lbs. cod filets

Directions:

1.   Place a large saucepan on medium high fire. Place a trivet inside saucepan and fill pan halfway with water. Cover and bring to a boil.

2. Meanwhile in a heat-proof dish that fits inside saucepan, layer half of the halved cherry tomatoes. Season with pepper.

3. Add filets on top of tomatoes and season with pepper. Drizzle oil. Sprinkle 3/4s of thyme on top and the smashed garlic.

4. Cover top of fish with remaining cherry tomatoes and place dish on trivet. Cover dish with foil.

5. Cover pan and steam for 15 minutes.

6. Serve and enjoy.

Nutrition:

Calories: 263.2; Carbs: 21.8g; Protein: 27.8g; Fats: 7.2g; Saturated Fat: 1.1g; Sodium: 264mg

Steamed Veggie and Lemon Pepper Salmon

Preparation time: 10 minutes

Servings: 4

Cooking time: 15 minutes

Ingredients:

- 1 carrot, peeled and julienned
- 1 red bell pepper, julienned
- 1 zucchini, julienned
- ½ lemon, sliced thinly
- 1 tsp. pepper
- ½ tsp. salt
- 1/2-lb salmon filet with skin on
- A dash of tarragon

Directions:

1. Place a large saucepan on medium high fire. Place a trivet inside saucepan and fill pan halfway with water. Cover and bring to a boil.

2. Meanwhile in a heat-proof dish that fits inside saucepan, add salmon with skin side

down. Season with pepper. Add slices of lemon on top.

3. Place the julienned vegetables on top of salmon and season with tarragon. Cover top of fish with remaining cherry tomatoes and place dish on trivet. Cover dish with foil.

4. Cover pan and steam for 15 minutes.

5. Serve and enjoy.

Nutrition:

Calories: 216.2; Carbs: 4.1g; Protein: 35.1g; Fats: 6.6g; Saturated Fat: 1.5g; Sodium: 332mg

Steamed Fish with Scallions and Ginger

Preparation time: 10 minutes

Servings: 3

Cooking time: 15 minutes

Ingredients:

- ¼ cup chopped cilantro
- ¼ cup julienned scallions
- 2 tbsp julienned ginger

- 1 tbsp peanut oil
- 1-lb Tilapia filets
- 1 tsp. garlic
- 1 tsp. minced ginger
- 2 tbsp rice wine
- 1 tbsp low sodium soy sauce

Directions:

1.   In a heat-proof dish that fits inside saucepan, add garlic, minced ginger, rice wine, and soy sauce. Mix well. Add the Tilapia filet and marinate for half an hour, while turning over at half time.

2. Place a large saucepan on medium high fire. Place a trivet inside saucepan and fill pan halfway with water. Cover and bring to a boil.

3. Cover dish of fish with foil and place on trivet.

4. Cover pan and steam for 15 minutes.

5. Serve and enjoy.

Nutrition:

Calories: 219; Carbs: 4.5g; Protein: 31.8g; Fats: 8.2g; Saturated Fat: 1.9g; Sodium: 252mg

Steamed Tilapia with Green Chutney

Preparation time: 10 minutes

Servings: 3

Cooking time: 10 minutes

Ingredients:

- 1-pound tilapia fillets, divided into 3
- ½ cup green commercial chutney

Directions:

1. Place a large saucepan on medium high fire. Place a trivet inside saucepan and fill pan halfway with water. Cover and bring to a boil.

2. Cut 3 pieces of 15-inch lengths foil.

3. In one foil, place one filet in the middle and 1/3 of chutney. Fold over the foil and seal the filet inside. Repeat process for remaining fish.

4. Place packet on trivet. Cover and steam for 10 minutes.

5. Serve and enjoy.

Nutrition:

Calories: 151.5; Carbs: 1.1g; Protein: 30.7g; Fats: 2.7g; Saturated Fat: .9g; Sodium: 79mg

Creamy Haddock with Kale

Preparation time: 10 minutes

Servings: 5

Cooking time: 10 minutes

Ingredients:

- 1 tbsp olive oil
- 1 onion, chopped
- 2 cloves of garlic, minced
- 2 cups chicken broth
- 1 teaspoon crushed red pepper flakes
- 1-pound wild Haddock fillets
- ½ cup heavy cream
- 1 tablespoons basil
- 1 cup kale leaves, chopped
- Pepper to taste

Directions:

1. Place a heavy bottomed pot on medium high fire and heat pot for 3 minutes.

2. Once hot, add oil and stir around to coat pot with oil.

3. Sauté the onion and garlic for 5 minutes.

4. Add remaining ingredients, except for basil and mix well.

5. Cover, bring to a boil, lower fire to a simmer, and simmer for 5 minutes.

6. Serve and enjoy with a sprinkle of basil.

Nutrition:

Calories: 130.5; Carbs: 5.5g; Protein: 35.7g; Fats: 14.5g; Saturated Fat: 5.2g; Sodium: 278mg

Coconut Curry Sea Bass

Preparation time: 10 minutes

Servings: 3

Cooking time: 15 minutes

Ingredients:

- 1 can coconut milk
- Juice of 1 lime, freshly squeezed
- 1 tablespoon red curry paste
- 1 teaspoon coconut aminos
- 1 teaspoon honey
- 2 teaspoons sriracha
- 2 cloves of garlic, minced
- 1 teaspoon ground turmeric
- 1 tablespoon curry powder
- ¼ cup fresh cilantro
- Pepper

Directions:

1. Place a heavy bottomed pot on medium high fire.

2. Mix in all ingredients.

3. Cover, bring to a boil, lower fire to a simmer, and simmer for 5 minutes.

4. Serve and enjoy.

Nutrition:

Calories: 241.8; Carbs: 12.8g; Protein: 3.1g; Fats: 19.8g; Saturated Fat: 17g; Sodium: 19mg

Stewed Cod Filet with tomatoes

Preparation time: 10 minutes

Servings: 6

Cooking time: 15 minutes

Ingredients:

- 1 tbsp olive oil
- 1 onion, sliced
- 1 ½ pounds fresh cod fillets
- Pepper
- 1 lemon juice, freshly squeezed
- 1 can diced tomatoes

Directions:

1. Place a heavy bottomed pot on medium high fire and heat pot for 3 minutes.

2. Once hot, add oil and stir around to coat pot with oil.

3. Sauté the onion for 2 minutes. Stir in diced tomatoes and cook for 5 minutes.

4. Add cod filet and season with pepper.

5. Cover, bring to a boil, lower fire to a simmer, and simmer for 5 minutes.

6. Serve and enjoy with freshly squeezed lemon juice.

Nutrition:

Calories: 106.4; Carbs: 2.5g; Protein: 17.8g; Fats: 2.8g; Saturated Fat: .4g; Sodium: 381mg

Lemony Parmesan Shrimps

Preparation time: 10 minutes

Servings: 4

Cooking time: 15 minutes

Ingredients:

- 1 tablespoon olive oil
- ½ cup onion, chopped
- 3 cloves of garlic, minced
- 1-pound shrimps, peeled and deveined
- ½ cup parmesan cheese, low fat

- 1 cup spinach, shredded
- ½ cup chicken broth, low sodium
- ¼ cup water
- Pepper

Directions:

1.   Place a heavy bottomed pot on medium high fire and heat pot for 3 minutes.

2. Once hot, add oil and stir around to coat pot with oil.

3. Sauté the onion and garlic for 5 minutes. Stir in shrimps and cook for 2 minutes.

4. Add remaining ingredients, except for parmesan.

5. Cover, bring to a boil, lower fire to a simmer, and simmer for 5 minutes.

6. Serve and enjoy with a sprinkle of parmesan.

Nutrition:

Calories: 252.6; Carbs: 5.4g; Protein: 33.9g; Fats: 10.6g; Saturated Fat: 3.2g; Sodium: 344mg

Tuna 'n Carrots Casserole

Preparation time: 10 minutes

Servings: 4

Cooking time: 12 minutes

Ingredients:

- 2 carrots, peeled and chopped
- ¼ cup diced onions
- 1 cup frozen peas
- ¾ cup milk
- 2 cans tuna in water, drained
- 1 can cream of celery soup
- 1 tbsp olive oil
- ½ cup water
- 2 eggs beaten
- Pepper

Directions:

1. Place a heavy bottomed pot on medium high fire and heat pot for 3 minutes.

2. Once hot, add oil and stir around to coat pot with oil.

3. Sauté the onion and carrots for 3 minutes.

4. Add remaining ingredients and mix well.

5. Bring to a boil while stirring constantly, cook until thickened around 5 minutes.

6. Serve and enjoy.

Nutrition:

Calories: 281.3; Carbs: 14.3g; Protein: 24.3g; Fats: 14.1g; Saturated Fat: 3.7g; Sodium: 275mg

Sweet-Ginger Scallops

Preparation time: 10 minutes

Servings: 3

Cooking time: 15 minutes

Ingredients:

- 1-pound sea scallops, shells removed
- ½ cup coconut aminos
- 3 tablespoons maple syrup
- ½ teaspoon garlic powder
- ½ teaspoon ground ginger

Directions:

1. In a heat-proof dish that fits inside saucepan, add all ingredients. Mix well.

2. Place a large saucepan on medium high fire. Place a trivet inside saucepan and fill pan halfway with water. Cover and bring to a boil.

3. Cover dish of scallops with foil and place on trivet.

4. Cover pan and steam for 10 minutes. Let it rest in pan for another 5 minutes.

5. Serve and enjoy.

Nutrition:

Calories: 233.4; Carbs: 23.7g; Protein: 31.5g; Fats: 1.4g; Saturated Fat: .4g; Sodium: 153mg

Savory Lobster Roll

Preparation time: 10 minutes

Servings: 6

Cooking time: 20 minutes

Ingredients:

- 1 ½ cups chicken broth, low sodium
- 2 teaspoon old bay seasoning
- 2 pounds lobster tails, raw and in the shell
- 1 lemon, halved
- 3 scallions, chopped
- 1 teaspoon celery seeds

Directions:

1. Place a heavy bottomed pot on medium high fire and add all ingredients and ½ of the lemon.

2. Cover, bring to a boil, lower fire to a simmer, and simmer for 15 minutes.

3. Let it rest for another 5 minutes.

4. Serve and enjoy with freshly squeezed lemon juice.

Nutrition:

Calories: 209; Carbs: 1.9g; Protein: 38.2g; Fats: 5.4g; Saturated Fat: 1.4g; Sodium: 288mg

Garlic 'n Tomatoes on Mussels

Preparation time: 10 minutes

Servings: 6

Cooking time: 15 minutes

Ingredients:

- ¼ cup white wine
- ½ cup water
- 3 Roma tomatoes, chopped
- 2 cloves of garlic, minced
- 1 bay leaf
- 2 pounds mussels, scrubbed
- ½ cup fresh parsley, chopped
- 1 tbsp oil
- Pepper

Directions:

1. Place a heavy bottomed pot on medium high fire and heat pot for 3 minutes.

2. Once hot, add oil and stir around to coat pot with oil.

3. Sauté the garlic, bay leaf, and tomatoes for 5 minutes.

4. Add remaining ingredients, except for parsley and mussels. Mix well.

5. Add mussels.

6. Cover, bring to a boil, and boil for 5 minutes.

7. Serve and enjoy with a sprinkle of parsley and discard any unopened mussels.

Nutrition:

Calories: 172.8; Carbs: 10.2g; Protein: 19.5g; Fats: 6g; Saturated Fat: 1.1g; Sodium: 261mg

Lobster Tarragon Stew

Preparation time: 10 minutes

Servings: 4

Cooking time: 30 minutes

Ingredients:

- 1 tablespoon olive oil
- 2 onions, diced
- 2 cloves of garlic, minced
- 1 carrot, chopped
- 2 lobsters, shelled
- 1-pound ripe tomatoes, chopped
- 2 tablespoon tomato paste
- 1/3 clam juice
- 1 tablespoon tarragon

Directions:

1.   Place a heavy bottomed pot on medium high fire and heat pot for 3 minutes.

2. Once hot, add oil and stir around to coat pot with oil.

3. Sauté the onion, tomatoes and garlic for 10 minutes.

4. Stir in tomato paste, clam juice, and carrot. Cook for 5 minutes.

5. Add lobsters and mix well.

6. Cover and simmer for 5 minutes.

7. Serve and enjoy a sprinkle of tarragon.

Nutrition:

Calories: 149.9; Carbs: 13.3g; Protein: 14.5g; Fats: 4.3g; Saturated Fat: 1g; Sodium: 341mg

Easy Steamed Crab Legs

Preparation time: 10 minutes

Servings: 4

Cooking time: 10 minutes

Ingredients:

- 2 pounds frozen crab legs
- 4 tablespoons low fat butter
- 1 tablespoon lemon juice, freshly squeezed

Directions:

1. Place a heavy bottomed pot on medium high fire, fill with 5 cups water and bring to a boil.

2. Add crab legs, cover and steam for 10 minutes. Once done, turn off fire and let it rest for 5 minutes.

3. Meanwhile, in a microwave safe bowl, melt butter. Once melted, add lemon juice and mix well.

4. Serve crab legs with lemon-butter dip on the side.

Nutrition:

Calories: 201.9; Carbs: 2.2g; Protein: 44g; Fats: 1.9g; Saturated Fat: .3g; Sodium: 297mg

Tasty Corn and Clam Stew

Preparation time: 10 minutes

Servings: 4

Cooking time: 25 minutes

Ingredients:

- 1-lb clam
- 1 cup frozen corn
- ½ cup water
- 4 cloves garlic
- 1 tsp. oil
- 1 tsp. celery seeds
- 1 tsp. Cajun seasoning

Directions:

1. Place a nonstick saucepan on medium high fire and heat pot for 3 minutes.

2. Once hot, add oil and stir around to coat pot with oil.

3. Sauté the garlic for a minute.

4. Add remaining ingredients, except for clams and mix well. Cook for 3 minutes.

5. Stir in clams.

6. Cover, bring to a boil, lower fire to a simmer, and simmer for 5 minutes.

7. Serve and enjoy. Discard any unopened clam.

Nutrition:

Calories: 120; Carbs: 23.2g; Protein: 2.3g; Fats: 2g;
Saturated Fat: .2g; Sodium: 466mg

Seafood Curry Recipe from Japan

Preparation time: 10 minutes

Servings: 4

Cooking time: 30 minutes

Ingredients:

- 3 onions, chopped
- 2 cloves of garlic, minced
- 1-inch ginger, grated
- 1 tsp. oil
- 3 cups water

- 1 2-inch long kombu or dried kelp
- 6 shiitake mushrooms, halved
- 12 manila clams, scrubbed
- 6 ounces medium-sized shrimps, peeled and deveined
- 6 ounces bay scallops
- 1 package Japanese curry roux
- ¼ apple, sliced

Directions:

1.   Place a heavy bottomed pot on medium high fire and heat pot for 3 minutes.

2. Once hot, add oil and stir around to coat pot with oil.

3. Sauté the onion, ginger and garlic for 5 minutes.

4. Add remaining ingredients and mix well.

5. Cover, bring to a boil, lower fire to a simmer, and simmer for 5 minutes. Let it rest for 5 minutes.

6. Serve and enjoy. Discard any unopened clams.

Nutrition:

Calories: 183.7; Carbs: 17.9g; Protein: 22.4g; Fats: 2.5g; Saturated Fat: .5g; Sodium: 294mg

Steamed Asparagus and Shrimps

Preparation time: 10 minutes

Servings: 6

Cooking time: 25 minutes

Ingredients:

- 1-pound shrimps, peeled and deveined
- 1 bunch asparagus, trimmed
- 1 teaspoon oil
- ½ tablespoon Cajun seasoning

Directions:

1. In a heat-proof dish that fits inside saucepan, add all ingredients. Mix well.

2. Place a large saucepan on medium high fire. Place a trivet inside saucepan and fill pan halfway with water. Cover and bring to a boil.

3. Cover dish with foil and place on trivet.

4. Cover pan and steam for 10 minutes. Let it rest in pan for another 5 minutes.

5. Serve and enjoy.

Nutrition:

Calories: 79.8; Carbs: .4g; Protein: 15.5g; Fats: 1.8g; Saturated Fat: .3g; Sodium: 209mg

Coconut Milk Sauce over Crabs

Preparation time: 10 minutes

Servings: 6

Cooking time: 20 minutes

Ingredients:

- 2-pounds crab quartered
- 1 can coconut milk
- 1 lemongrass stalk
- 1 thumb-size ginger, sliced
- 1 onion, chopped
- 3 cloves of garlic, minced
- Pepper

Directions:

1. Place a heavy bottomed pot on medium high fire and add all ingredients.

2. Cover, bring to a boil, lower fire to a simmer, and simmer for 10 minutes.

3. Serve and enjoy.

Nutrition:

Calories: 244.1; Carbs: 6.3g; Protein: 29.3g; Fats: 11.3g; Saturated Fat: 8.8g; Sodium: 356mg

Cajun Shrimp Boil

Preparation time: 10 minutes

Servings: 4

Cooking time: 40 minutes

Ingredients:

- 2 corn on the cobs, halved
- 1/2 kielbasa sausage, sliced into 2-inch pieces
- 1 cup chicken broth, low sodium
- 1 tablespoon old bay seasoning
- 1 tsp celery seeds
- 4 garlic cloves, smashed
- 1 teaspoon crushed red peppers
- 4 small potatoes, brushed and halved
- 1 onion, chopped
- 1-pound shrimps
- 1 tbsp olive oil
- Pepper

Directions:

1.   Place a heavy bottomed pot on medium high fire and heat pot for 3 minutes.

2. Once hot, add oil and stir around to coat pot with oil.

3. Sauté the garlic, onion, potatoes, and sausage for 5 minutes.

4. Stir in corn, broth, old bay, celery seeds, and red peppers. Cover and cook for 5 minutes.

5. Stir in shrimps and cook for another 5 minutes.
6. Serve and enjoy.

Nutrition:

Calories: 549.5; Carbs: 69.4g; Protein: 44.8g; Fats: 10.3g; Saturated Fat: 2.1g; Sodium: 289mg